LATIN
Playalong *for* Clarinet

C000139285

WISE PUBLICATIONS
London/New York/Paris/Sydney/Copenhagen/Madrid/Tokyo

Exclusive Distributors:
Music Sales Limited
8/9 Frith Street, London W1D 3JB, England.
Music Sales Pty Limited
120 Rothschild Avenue, Rosebery, NSW 2018, Australia.

Order No. AM966064
ISBN 0-7119-8366-6
This book © Copyright 2001 by Wise Publications.

Compiled by Nick Crispin.
Music arranged by Jack Long.
Music processed by Enigma Music Production Services.
Cover photography by George Taylor.
Printed in the United Kingdom by Page Bros., Norwich, Norfolk.

CD produced by Music By Design.
Instrumental solos by John Whelan.
Engineered by Kester Sims.

Your Guarantee of Quality:
As publishers, we strive to produce every book to
the highest commercial standards.
The music has been freshly engraved and the book has been
carefully designed to minimise awkward page turns and
to make playing from it a real pleasure.
Particular care has been given to specifying acid-free, neutral-sized
paper made from pulps which have not been elemental chlorine bleached.
This pulp is from farmed sustainable forests and was
produced with special regard for the environment.
Throughout, the printing and binding have been planned to
ensure a sturdy, attractive publication which should give years of enjoyment.
If your copy fails to meet our high standards,
please inform us and we will gladly replace it.

Music Sales' complete catalogue describes thousands of
titles and is available in full colour sections by subject,
direct from Music Sales Limited.
Please state your areas of interest and send a
cheque/postal order for £1.50 for postage to:
Music Sales Limited, Newmarket Road, Bury St. Edmunds, Suffolk IP33 3YB.

www.musicsales.com

Clarinet Fingering Chart

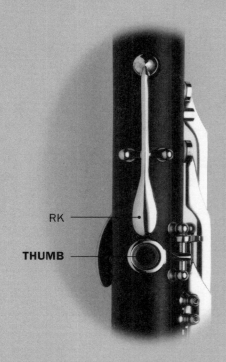

RK

THUMB

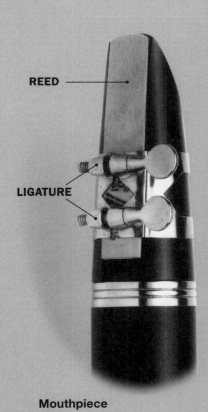

REED

LIGATURE

Mouthpiece

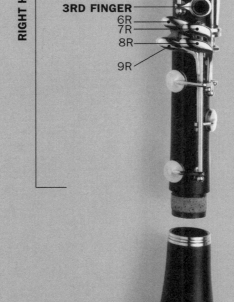

1L
2L
1ST FINGER

2ND FINGER
3L

3RD FINGER
4L

1R
2R
3R
4R

5L
6L
7L

1ST FINGER

2ND FINGER
5R

3RD FINGER

6R
7R
8R

9R

LEFT HAND

RIGHT HAND

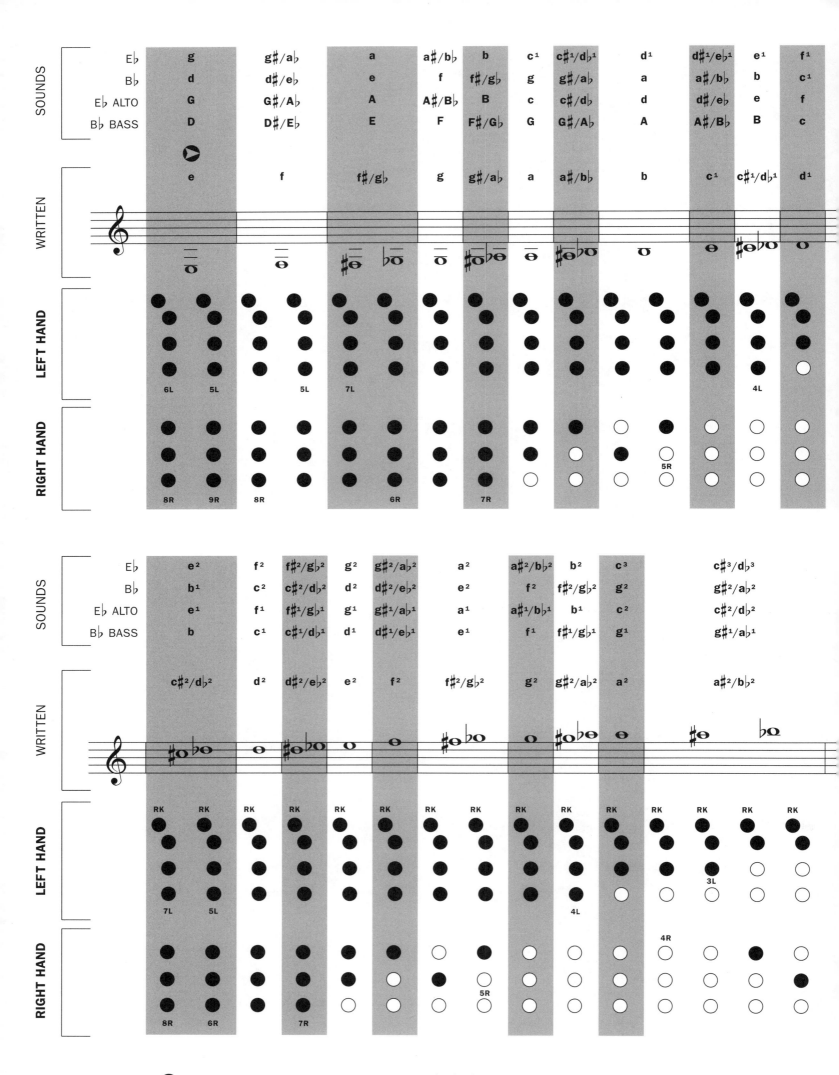

Indicates the lower limit of the best playing range for E♭, B♭, E♭ Alto and B♭ Bass Clarinets

Indicates the upper limit of the best playing range for E♭ and B♭ Clarinets

Indicates the upper limit of the best playing range for E♭ Alto and B♭ Bass Clarinets

Dos Gardenias

Words & Music by Isolina Carrillo

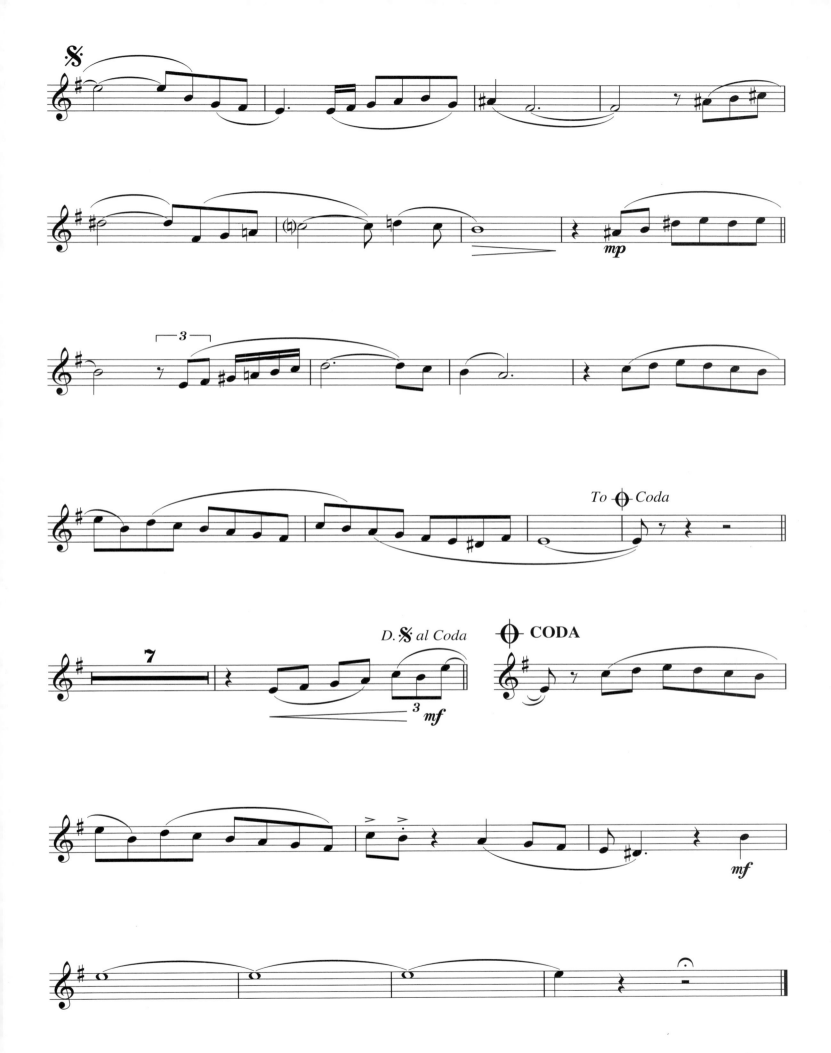

Besame Mucho

Words & Music by Consuelo Velazquez

9

The Girl From Ipanema
(Garota De Ipanema)

Original Words by Vinicius De Moraes
Music by Antonio Carlos Jobim
English Words by Norman Gimbel

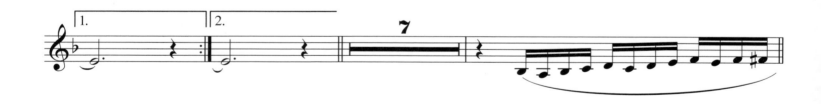

Guantanamera

Words Adapted by Julian Orbon from a poem by José Marti
Music Adaptation by Pete Seeger & Julian Orbon

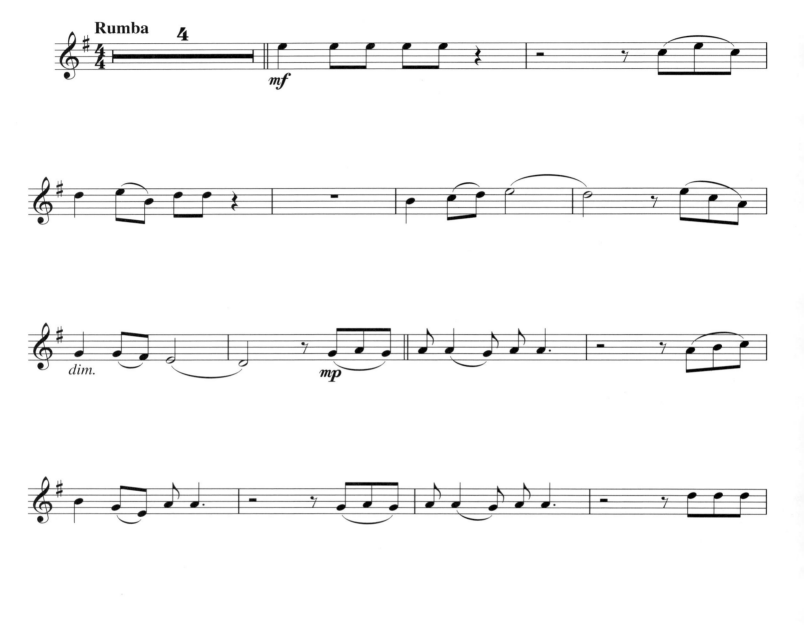

p poco a poco cresc.   *mp*

mf

dim.

rit.

mp

La Bamba

Traditional
Adapted & Arranged by Ritchie Valens

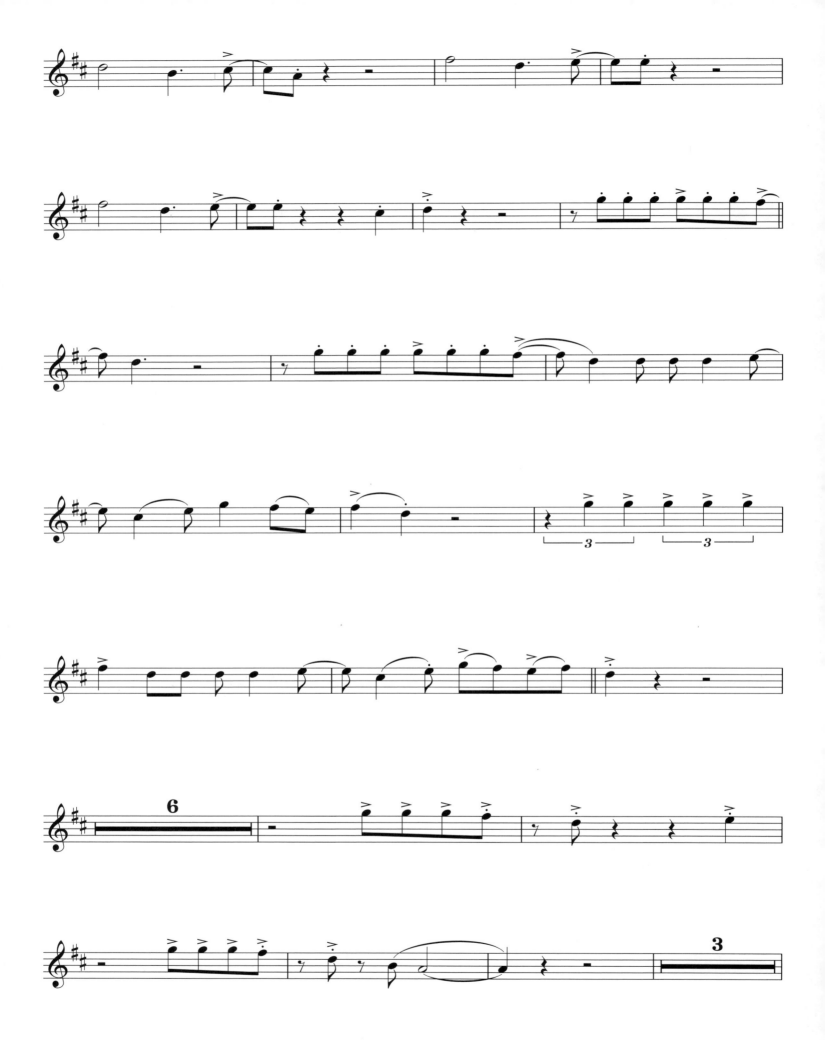

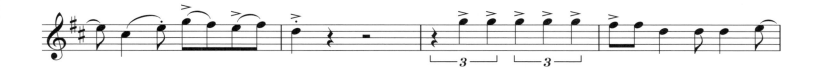

Lambada

Words & Music by Ulises Hermosa, Gonzales Hermosa, Alberto Maravi, Marcia Ferreira & Jose Ari
Music by Ulises Hermosa & Gonzales Hermosa

Medium tempo

Mas Que Nada

Words & Music by Jorge Ben

Perhaps, Perhaps, Perhaps (Quizas, Quizas, Quizas)

Original Words & Music by Osvaldo Farres
English Words by Joe Davis

Sway (Quien Sera)

Original Words & Music by Pablo Beltran Ruiz
English Words by Normal Gimbel

Oye Como Va

Words & Music by Tito Puente